Mister Maker™

Let's Make It!

Contents

2

Mmmm... what shall we make today?

3

Hello, there!
Mister Maker here!
Welcome to my fantastic book.
It's packed full of great things for
you to make so you'll never run
out of ideas. These pages will
show you some of the things to
look out for in the book. Are you
ready to start? You are?
Well, let's make it!

Mister
Maker

Hey, look – it's those funny
shapes! They'll pop up
throughout the book where
you least expect them!

triangle

rectangle

circle

square

Stop the clock!

Look out for the clocks at the top of the page.

When you've only got a bit of time to make something, go to the Minute Makes section where Tocky will help you along.

When you've got a bit longer, then the Medium Makes section is the place to be.

When you've got EVEN longer, go to the Massive Makes section!

Check out these crazy frames! One of these on the page means your make will look so good you'll want to frame it!

Before you start any make, you'll need some things from the Doodle Drawers such as a glue stick, scissors and a cauliflower... oh no, that's for my tea later!

Doodle Drawers

glue stick

scissors

air drying clay

felt tip pen

paint

This sign means you might want an adult to help you.

This sign means you should be careful with your scissors because scissors are sharp.

Foam butterfly

Doodle Drawers

3 pieces of kitchen foam

scissors

straw

sticky tape

glue stick

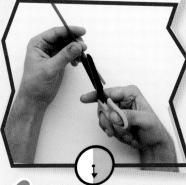

1 Fold a rectangle-shaped piece of kitchen foam in half. Cut out half a butterfly shape.

2 Snip down into the top of your straw. You can now pull the two bits apart to make the butterfly's antennae.

3 Unfold your butterfly shape. Stick the straw antennae onto the butterfly with sticky tape.

4 Cut shapes out of the other pieces of kitchen foam. Stick them on to your butterfly to make it colourful.

Let's move quickly!

Try making a ladybird like me!

Doodle Drawers

- card
- felt tip pen
- scissors
- glue stick
- wooden peg
- 2 white stickers

1 On the card, draw an arch shape for the elephant's body and give it two big ears. Draw a trunk and cut all the bits out.

2 Glue the wooden peg to your elephant body and glue your trunk on top of the peg. You'll have to move very quickly!

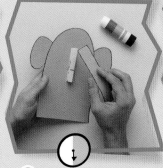

3 Stick the stickers on for eyes.

Afterwards you can dot the eyes and give your elephant wrinkles on its trunk and toes.

Peg holders are great for photos!

Bug in a jar

1 Roll the clay into any shape you like.

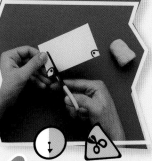

2 Draw some eyes onto white card and cut them out. Your bug can have as many buggy eyes as you want!

3 Push the eyes into the top of the clay. Then put your bug on the jar lid and screw the jar on top.

Doodle Drawers

- white card
- scissors
- modelling clay
- small plastic jar with a lid
- felt tip pen

Why not try making a crazy hairy bug by adding a feather on top?

Snake pot

1 Roll a lump of clay into a long sausage shape. Be quick and careful as you don't want the clay to break.

2 Start to twirl your clay round and build it up into a pot shape.

3 Turn up the end of the snake to make a head. Use two small bits of clay to make snake eyes. With a pencil, dot the eyes and leave the pot to dry.

When you have more time, you can paint your slithery snake any colour you like.

Pencil pet

Doodle Drawers

feathers

pencil

pipe cleaner

sponge

googly eyes

scissors

glue stick

Hurry up!

1 Take two feathers and hold them against a pencil. Wrap the pipe cleaner round the pencil to hold them in place.

2 Stick two googly eyes onto the pipe cleaner.

3 Cut out a small triangle of sponge for your pet's beak. Stick your beak on with glue and you're done!

Get sticking!

Pop-up card

Doodle Drawers

card

felt tip pen

strip of paper

glue stick

1 Fold the card in half and draw a clown on the inside. Give him a nice round nose and a funny clown hat.

2 Start folding your strip of paper over one way and then over the other way like a fan. This is a bit fiddly!

3 Put glue on either end of the fan and stick it into the card. Doesn't your clown look brilliant? What do you think, Tocky?

Stop clowning around!

You could make lots of different pop-up cards. Try this pretty ballerina, which uses pink paper for her tutu.

Or what about this cupcake with purple paper for the icing? Yummy!

Cork boat

Doodle Drawers

scissors

straw

plastic lid

sticky tape

hole punch

triangle-shaped piece of paper

PVA glue

8 corks

1 Using your scissors, make three slits in the top of the straw. Be careful because scissors are sharp.

2 Place the straw on your lid using the slits you made. Stick it down with sticky tape.

3 Use a hole punch to put one hole in the bottom of your triangle-shaped piece of paper and one in the top. This is your boat's sail.

How about making a boat with different coloured paper and two sails? Give it a go!

4 Carefully feed the straw through the holes in the sail.

5 Put glue on the bottom of the lid and stick your corks on. Now your boat is ready to set sail.

Straw panpipes

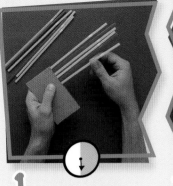

1 Push the straws through the holes in the corrugated cardboard.

2 Cut diagonally across the straws. Be careful because scissors are very sharp. Take a deep breath and blow!

Time's up!

Afterwards, you can paint your panpipes so they both look and sound brilliant.

Doodle Drawers

straws

corrugated cardboard

scissors

Concertina puppet

Doodle Drawers

card

felt tip pen

2 straws

sticky tape

googly eye

1 First rip a piece of card into a fish shape.

2 Draw a mouth and other details on your fish.

3 Fold the paper fish over one way and then over the other way until it is completely folded.

4 Stick two straws on the back. Finish it off by sticking a googly eye on.

Now you can do a puppet show!

Pom-pom acrobat

Doodle Drawers

- pom-pom
- glue stick
- pipe cleaner
- pencil
- 2 bendy straws
- googly eyes

1 Take your pom-pom and pull it apart a bit in the middle. Stick the pipe cleaner in the pom-pom and push the sides of the pom-pom together.

2 Bend the pipe cleaner ends upwards and twirl them round the pencil. This is your acrobat.

3 Bend two straws and push them together. This is your acrobat's bar.

4 Take the acrobat off the pencil and feed it onto the straw. This is fiddly!

5 Stick googly eyes on the pom-pom. Now you can spin your acrobat round the bar. Look how quickly it goes!

1...2...3... spin!

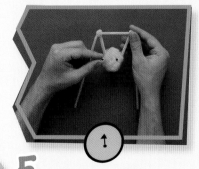

You could even make a pom-pom ant acrobat using three pom-poms. Give your ant six legs and some antennae.

How many circles can you see?

Dog card

Doodle Drawers

triangle-shaped piece of card

white paper

felt tip pens

scissors

glue stick

1 Fold over each corner of the triangle-shaped piece of card to make dog ears.

2 Cut two circles from white paper and draw eyes on them. Stick them on the card.

3 Draw on your dog's other details. Give him a nose and a smiley mouth.

When you've finished your dog, you can write a message under his ears and give it to a friend. Dog cards are great!

Splat monster pen pal

Doodle Drawers

air drying clay

crayon

1 Roll some clay into a ball. Squidge it into a nice monster shape.

2 Next, roll two smaller bits of clay into two balls for the eyes. Put these on top of your monster.

3 Use the crayon to dot the eyes. Draw a mouth and make a hole that can hold a pen or crayon.

After your pen pal is dry, you can paint it.

Eeek, eeek!

Mouse finger puppet

Doodle Drawers

half-circle piece of card

sticky tape

scissors

rectangle-shaped piece of card

glue stick

2 small circles of paper

pipe cleaner

1 Roll the half-circle piece of card into a cone and stick it with tape. This is a bit fiddly!

2 Pinch the end of the cone. Use your scissors to make a slit in the top of the cone.

3 Fold the rectangle-shaped piece of card in half and cut out an ear shape.

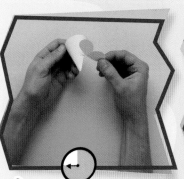

4 Unfold the ears and put them in the slit in the cone.

5 Stick two circles of paper on either side of your cone for eyes. Stick the pipe cleaner in the back of the cone for a tail.

Aren't finger puppets great?

When you have more than a minute, add details such as dots for the eyes.

Birthday badge

2 small cake cases

large cake case

glue stick

paper

felt tip pen

scissors

ribbon

1 Stick a small cake case inside the large cake case. Stick another small case inside this.

2 Cut out a small circle of paper that will fit in the cake case and stick it down. This make has got a lot of sticking!

3 Draw a picture of a birthday cake on the circle of paper.

4 Tie a piece of ribbon into a bow and stick it on the front of your beautiful birthday badge!

Happy birthday to you!

Spoon bug

1 Let's go! First roll a lump of clay into a ball.

2 Squidge the clay into the spoon. Make sure it's stuck in!

3 Cut the three cotton buds in half for the bug's legs. Stick each one into the clay.

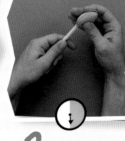

How about trying a spider with eight pipe cleaner legs?

Have you got the bug?

When the clay has dried, flip the bug out and paint it.

When you have more than a minute, you can decorate your tube.

Torch projector

Doodle Drawers

white coloured pencil

crisp tube with a lid

rectangle-shaped piece of black paper

scissors

torch

glue stick

Lights off!

Why not try making a bat torch projector? Simply draw a bat instead of a spider on your paper. Bats love hanging around at night!

1 Fold the rectangle-shaped piece of black paper in half. With the white coloured pencil, draw half a spider close to the fold.

2 Cut your spider shape out. This can be a bit fiddly!

3 Unfold the spider shape and stick it onto the outside of the crisp tube lid. Almost done!

4 Turn your torch on and put it in your crisp tube. Finally, put the lid on top and you have a shiny, spooky torch projector!

Doodle
Drawers

Pot that holds a lot

**strip of
black paper**

**glue
stick**

strip of
coloured paper

stickers   **stars**

**cardboard
pot**   **sticky
tape**

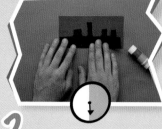

1 Tear the black
strip of paper up
and down into a
city scene.

2 Stick your torn
black paper onto
your coloured
strip of paper.

3 Add stickers
for the windows of
the buildings and
stick some stars in
the night sky.

4 Wrap the picture
around the pot and
stick it down with
tape. Now fill up
your pot!

Kitchen roll art

**Doodle
Drawers**

**piece of
kitchen roll**   **3 bowls of food
colouring**

1 Fold a
piece of
kitchen roll in
half and then
in half again.

2 Fold one
corner up to the
other to make a
triangle. Do the
same again to
make an even
smaller triangle.

3 Dip each
corner of the
kitchen paper
into a different
bowl of food
colouring.

After you've done all
the dipping, open up
your piece of
kitchen paper and
you've got a lovely
piece of art.

17

Sponge toast and beans

Doodle Drawers

felt tip pen

yellow kitchen sponge

orange tissue paper

scissors

orange paint

white paint and brown paint

plastic fork and knife

paintbrush

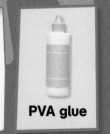

PVA glue

paper plate

Look at this fantastic plate of toast and beans. Doesn't it look real? All you need is a piece of kitchen sponge and some things from the Doodle Drawers. Let's get cooking!

1 Draw a toast shape on your kitchen sponge and cut it out. Be careful because scissors are very sharp.

2 Mix some white paint with brown paint and paint your sponge. Next, paint the edges with normal brown paint for the crusts.

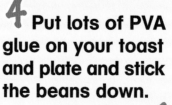

3 When the paint is dry, stick your toast to the plate. Then roll bits of tissue paper into balls for your beans.

4 Put lots of PVA glue on your toast and plate and stick the beans down.

5 For the baked bean sauce, mix some glue with some orange paint. Pour the mixture over your beans.

Be careful – the toast and beans may look good enough to eat but they are just a piece of brilliant art!

6 Finally, stick a plastic fork and knife on the plate and leave it to dry. You're done!

This is making me hungry!

Splat monster

Doodle Drawers

tube of runny paint

coloured paper

black felt tip pen

scissors

white paper

glue stick

1 Squeeze some paint on a piece of coloured paper. That's your first splat! Make lots of splats all over the page.

2 When the paint has dried, draw a monster shape on it. Your monster can have tentacles, two heads or anything you like.

Look out – there's a splat monster about!

3 Cut out two circles from your white paper and draw dots on them for eyes. Stick the eyes on your monster.

4 Finally, give your monster other features. You could add a mouth and crazy eyebrows. Then all you have to do is cut it out. What a brilliant splat monster!

Try making a dribble monster by dribbling your paint on the paper. Or what about adding some splodges? Go wild!

Space age city

PVA glue

black felt tip pen

silver paint

paintbrushes

plastic container

coloured paint

1 Mix silver paint with some PVA glue. Then paint a plastic container, such as a cup, with the mixture.

2 When the paint is dry, use your other paints to decorate your space age building.

3 Add details to your building with a pen. You can give it windows for the friendly aliens to see out of!

When you've done one, do the same with other containers and soon you'll have a whole space age city.

Pasta picture

Doodle Drawers

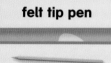

white paper

felt tip pen

coloured pencils

PVA glue

dried pasta tubes

1 You can make any pasta picture you like but let's try a curly haired woman. Draw a woman on your paper but don't give her any hair.

2 Colour your picture in however you like. This make is very easy but it'll look so good when it's finished you'll be able to frame it!

3 Put glue round the woman's head and stick on your pasta tubes. Make sure the tubes face up and it'll look like curly hair!

Do you like my new haircut?

Try using twisty pasta to make a twirly hair style or straight pasta called spaghetti to make this dog. She's even got a pretty bow!

Change your photos

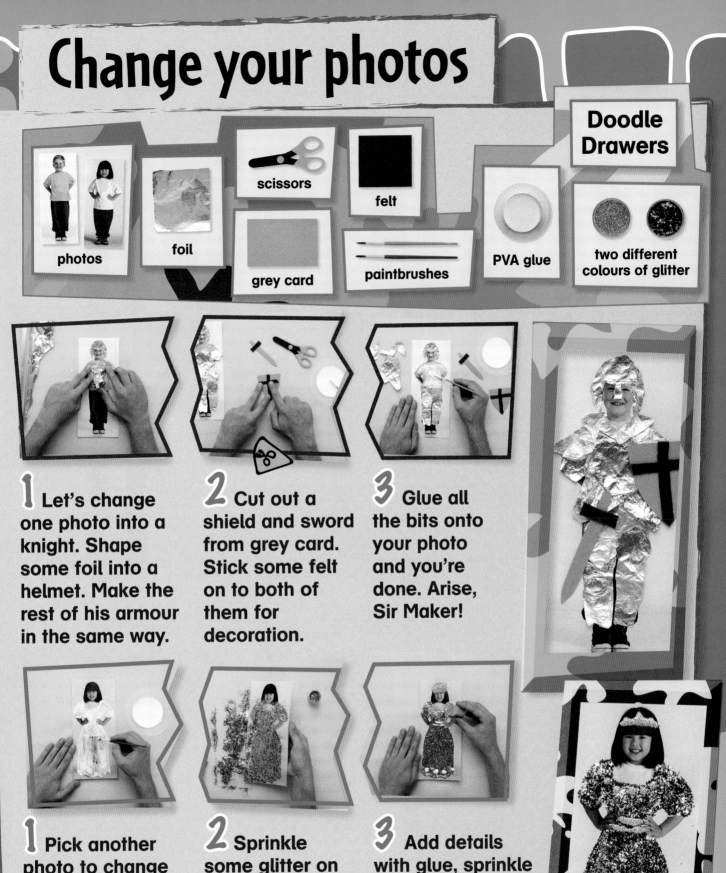

photos

foil

scissors

felt

grey card

paintbrushes

PVA glue

Doodle Drawers

two different colours of glitter

1 Let's change one photo into a knight. Shape some foil into a helmet. Make the rest of his armour in the same way.

2 Cut out a shield and sword from grey card. Stick some felt on to both of them for decoration.

3 Glue all the bits onto your photo and you're done. Arise, Sir Maker!

1 Pick another photo to change into a princess. Using glue and a paintbrush, paint a dress shape on your photo.

2 Sprinkle some glitter on the photo and shake off the extra glitter onto a piece of paper.

3 Add details with glue, sprinkle a different colour glitter over it and shake off the extra glitter. Hello, Princess Maker!

Ship in a jar

Doodle Drawers

- air drying clay
- glue stick
- blue food colouring
- piece of kitchen roll
- plastic jar with a lid
- bowl of rice
- scissors
- plastic spoon
- straw

Fit an ocean into a jar with its very own ship. Don't forget that your jar will need to be big enough to get your hand in! Let's set sail on the high seas!

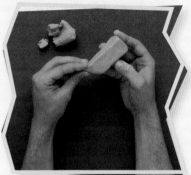

1 Add a few drops of blue food colouring to the rice. Stir it with the plastic spoon until the rice has turned blue.

2 Squeeze some clay into the shape of a ship. Give it a nice pointy end so it can glide through the sea.

3 Take two smaller bits of clay and shape them into cubes. Stick these on top of the ship. That's starting to look shipshape!

How many triangles can you see?

4 Take your piece of kitchen roll and cut off two corners. One should be big and one should be small. These are your sails.

5 Cut two bits off your straw. Make sure they are about the same size. Then stick one sail round each straw with glue stick.

6 Push the sails into the clay ship. Very carefully slide the ship in the jar and press it down hard so it doesn't move. Almost done!

7 Pour your blue rice into the jar. Don't forget to screw the lid back on. Finished!

A life on the ocean wave...

Cardboard cactus

Phew! The Old West is mighty hot and dry. Luckily this fantastic cardboard cactus never needs watering. Yee-ha!

You wouldn't want to get too close to a cactus. Its spikes are sharp!

Doodle Drawers

- ruler
- paintbrush
- 2 pieces of card
- dark green paint
- felt tip pens
- light green paint
- scissors

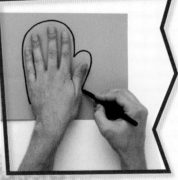

1 On one piece of card, draw around your hand and thumb in a mitten shape. This is your first cactus shape. Do the same with your second piece of card.

2 Cut your first cactus shape out, making sure you have a straight edge on the bottom. Do the same thing with the other cactus shape.

3 On one cactus shape, draw a line from the bottom up to about half way. On the other, draw a line from the top down to about half way.

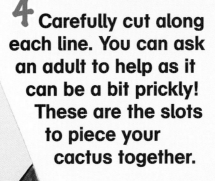

4 Carefully cut along each line. You can ask an adult to help as it can be a bit prickly! These are the slots to piece your cactus together.

Once you've made a cactus, try making a teepee using triangle-shaped pieces of card.

5 Time to paint your cactus. Use dark and light green paint and paint both sides.

6 Once the paint is dry, draw prickly spikes all over your cactus shapes.

7 Now all you need to do is slot the two pieces together. That looks brilliant!

Or how about a great fire to cook your cowboy dinners over?

Cat shower gel sign

Doodle Drawers

shower gel bottle with a hook

scissors

wool

white tissue paper

PVA glue

paintbrushes

PVA glue in a bowl

pencil

paints

felt tip pen

1 You can hang this sign on your door handle to tell people when you're awake! Clean out the bottle and cover it with scraps of tissue paper and PVA glue.

Miaow! I'm wide awake!

2 When it's dry, use a pencil to draw a wide awake cat on one side of the bottle and a sleepy cat on the other. Then you can paint it.

3 When the paint is dry, add some details with the felt tip pen. You can even give your cat a painted nose.

Zzzzzz.... zzzzzz!

4 Now all it needs are some wool whiskers. Cut up some small pieces of wool and stick them on your wide awake cat and your sleepy cat.

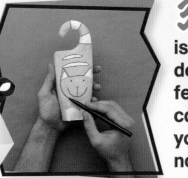

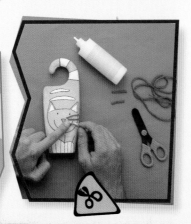

28

Peacock handprint picture

green paint

paper

white, yellow and blue paint

felt tip pen

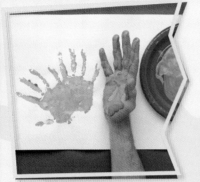

1 Cover the palm of your hand in green paint and press it on the paper. Then move your hand round and press it down again. Keep doing this to make a fan.

2 After washing your hand, dip the whole of your thumb in blue paint and press it down in the middle of your fan. This is the body.

3 Wash your hand again. Then decorate your peacock with blue, yellow and white dots using the tips of your fingers.

When your peacock is dry, use a felt tip pen to give him some eyes and legs. What beautiful feathers he has!

Blow picture

Doodle Drawers

paper

water

straw

felt tip pen

paint

paintbrush

Are you out of puff yet?

1 Mix some water into your paint to make it nice and runny.

2 Using your paintbrush, put a large blob of runny paint on your paper.

3 Now, take a deep breath! With your straw, blow the paint out in spikes to make a funny monster.

4 When you're happy with your crazy monster, give it some big buggy eyes with a pen.

Blow pictures are so easy! How about trying a man with spiky hair? Or what about a prickly hedgehog? Go wild!

Sliding eyes chicken

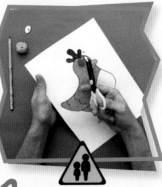

paper

black felt tip pen

coloured felt tip pens

modelling clay

1 On one piece of paper draw a chicken. Make sure the eyes are nice and big. Colour your picture in with chickeny colours!

2 Put some clay under your paper near the eyes. Use a pencil to make holes in the eyes. The pencil will go into the clay. Now you can cut the eyes out.

3 Cut out a long strip of paper and put it behind the holes in your chicken picture. Draw in two big eyes.

sticky tape

scissors

pencil

Get sliding!

4 Stick two smaller pieces of paper to the back of the picture. These will hold the strip in place. Make sure it can slide through easily.

Crocodile puppet

Doodle Drawers

paintbrush

2 thin rectangle-shaped boxes

green paint

white paper

black felt tip pen

scissors

glue stick

green card

sticky tape

2 pom-poms

Have you ever wanted to put on your own puppet show? Now you can with this fantastic crocodile puppet. There's no time to waste so you'd better make it snappy!

I'm hungry! What's for dinner?

1 Cut the flaps off one end of one box so it has an open end. Do the same with your other box.

2 Use sticky tape to stick the open ends of your boxes together. Time to make your puppet come to life!

3 Now paint your boxes a crocodile green colour. Don't forget to paint all over the boxes. Leave them to dry.

4 Stick two pom-poms near the open ends of your boxes. Draw two eyes on white paper and cut them out. Stick these on the pom-poms.

5 On green card, draw two arches for nostrils. Cut them out and stick them near your crocodile's mouth.

6 Cut a zigzag pattern out of a strip of white paper. This will make the top and bottom teeth for one side of the crocodile's mouth. Do the same again for the other side.

7 Stick the teeth on both sides of the mouth. Finish him off with two sharp front teeth cut out from white paper.

Busy city picture

Doodle Drawers

sticky tape

2 different coloured felt tip pens

paper

1 Take a piece of sticky tape and tape your two felt tip pens together. Now you can draw two lines at the same time!

2 Draw straight lines up, across and down on your piece of paper. These are your city's buildings. Don't they look like they're moving?

3 Now give your buildings doors and windows by adding squiggles and dots. This picture looks so good you'll be able to frame it.

It's always busy in the city!

How many rectangles can you see?

Multicoloured space picture

Doodle Drawers

white paper

black paint

crayons

paintbrush

plastic knife

washing-up liquid

This picture is out of this world!

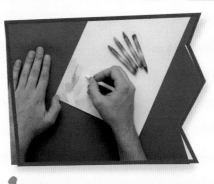

1 Colour in the piece of white paper with crayons. Make sure the page is covered in lots of colours.

2 Mix black paint with a few squirts of washing-up liquid. Careful – you don't want bubbly paint!

3 Use the paintbrush to cover your crayon picture completely with the paint mixture.

4 When the picture is dry, use the plastic knife to scrape a picture into the paint.

Buried treasure

Ha, ha, me shipmates! What does every good pirate need? Buried treasure, of course. And if you can't find any, how about making some? Let's get digging!

Doodle Drawers

- scissors
- paintbrush
- paper plate
- PVA glue
- piece of kitchen roll
- piece of cardboard box card
- black paint
- bronze paint
- felt tip pen

1 Put a paper plate on your piece of card and draw round it. This is your coin. Cut it out but be careful because scissors are very sharp.

2 Draw a treasure design on your coin. You could draw a king or queen's head, a simple pattern or whatever you like really!

3 Now go over all the drawn lines with glue. This is a bit fiddly so you could ask an adult to help. When that's all done, leave your coin to dry.

4 When the glue has dried, it will be see-through. Now you can paint the coin with black paint. Don't forget to paint both sides.

5 After the paint has dried, scrunch your kitchen roll up and use it to rub bronze paint over both sides of the coin. All done!

What a brilliant piece of buried treasure!

How many circles can you see?

Shell butterfly

Doodle Drawers

cardboard box card

paints

1 Start by painting your piece of card any colour you want. Make sure you paint the whole thing.

2 Put a line of pebbles in the middle of the card for the butterfly's body. Put one big shell on either side of the body.

3 Now you know where you want it all to go, stick it down! You can also add some wool for the antennae.

paintbrushes

pebbles

2 big shells

wool

scissors

PVA glue

 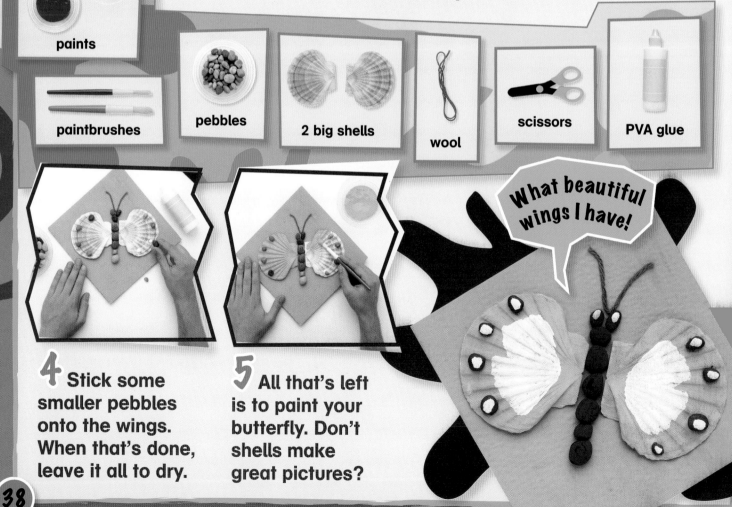

4 Stick some smaller pebbles onto the wings. When that's done, leave it all to dry.

5 All that's left is to paint your butterfly. Don't shells make great pictures?

What beautiful wings I have!

Wool doodle

1 Cut a long piece of wool and dip it into the bowl of glue. Make sure it's nice and covered. Place the wool on the card.

2 Start to make a doodly pattern with the wool. When you are happy with your pattern, leave it to dry.

3 Now it's time to make your picture look colourful. Use paint and the felt tip pen to colour in some of the spaces and all around your wool shapes.

4 Paint glue on bits of the picture. Sprinkle glitter over the gluey bits and shake off the extra glitter onto a piece of paper. This looks so good, you could frame it!

wool

scissors

PVA glue

cardboard box card

paints

paintbrushes

felt tip pen

glitter

Sandcastle

Doodle Drawers

play sand

2 kitchen roll tubes

paintbrush

scissors

PVA glue

large kitchen tray

I do like to be beside the seaside...

Don't you just love going to the beach? What could be better than playing in the sand? Well, how about making this sandcastle that will stay standing even after the tide has come in!

1 Right – let's get making! First of all, cut one of your kitchen roll tubes in half. Be careful because scissors are sharp.

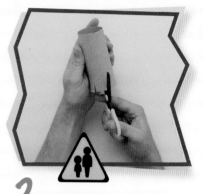

2 Take one of the halves and make snips round one end of the tube. This will be your turret. This is fiddly so you may want an adult to help.

3 Fold every other flap forward. Cut off these folded flaps very carefully. Your castle is taking shape!

4 Your turret needs a door so cut one out. This can be tricky too so you may want an adult to help again.

Give your castle a flag made out of paper and a straw.

Welcome to my castle!

5 Time for the most important bit! Fill your tray with sand. This is just like the beach!

6 Put glue all over your turret and roll it in the sand until it is completely covered. Now that you've done one turret, do exactly the same with your other kitchen roll tube.

Try covering a washing-up liquid bottle in sand. Put all your pieces together and you have a sandcastle that lasts forever!

Clay picture

Doodle Drawers

air drying clay

rolling pin

small box lid

old toy

glue spreader

straw

plastic fork

felt tip pen

paints

paintbrushes

Use any old bits and pieces you can find round the house to make this great clay picture. When you're done, you can hang it up for everyone to see!

1 Take some clay and roll it into your lid using the rolling pin. Don't worry if you don't have a rolling pin – you can use your hands to flatten the clay out.

2 Now, take your old toy and press it into the clay so that it leaves a print.

3 Build up the rest of the picture using other items. As we've got a fish in our picture, let's make some waves with a plastic fork and some reeds with a glue spreader or straw.

Get printing!

You can hang your picture up by threading ribbon or string through the hole that you made. Ask an adult to hang it on the wall, just like in an art gallery!

4 When you're done, push the end of the pen into the top of your piece of clay to make a hole. You'll use this to hang your picture on the wall.

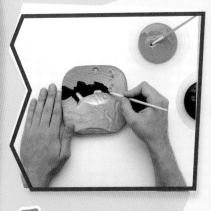

5 After your clay picture is dry, take it out of the lid and paint it. With your paint you can pick out the parts where your toys have been pushed in. What a brilliant picture!

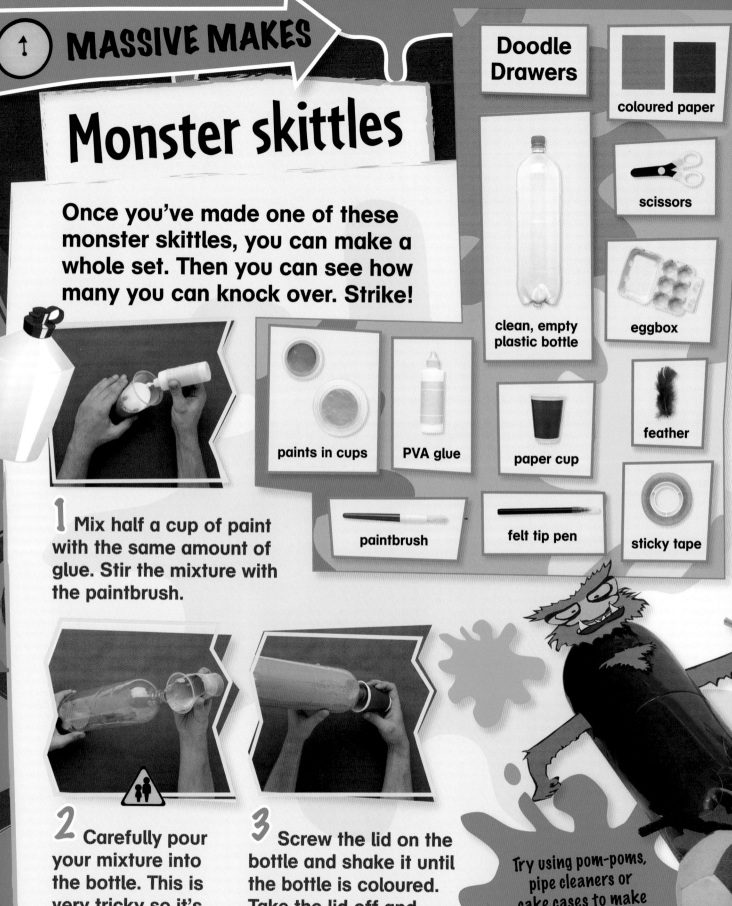

Monster skittles

Once you've made one of these monster skittles, you can make a whole set. Then you can see how many you can knock over. Strike!

Doodle Drawers

coloured paper

scissors

clean, empty plastic bottle

eggbox

paints in cups

PVA glue

paper cup

feather

paintbrush

felt tip pen

sticky tape

1 Mix half a cup of paint with the same amount of glue. Stir the mixture with the paintbrush.

2 Carefully pour your mixture into the bottle. This is very tricky so it's probably best to ask an adult to help you.

3 Screw the lid on the bottle and shake it until the bottle is coloured. Take the lid off and stand the bottle upside down in the cup. Leave it to dry overnight.

Try using pom-poms, pipe cleaners or cake cases to make your monster skittles look really monstrous!

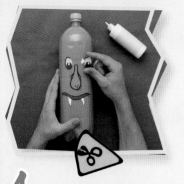

4 Morning! Put the lid back on your bottle. Now draw monster features on some coloured paper. Cut them out and stick them on the front of the bottle.

5 To make your monster's horns, cut out the pointy bits from the eggbox. Stick them on the side of your bottle.

6 When the horns are stuck down, paint them any colour that you like.

7 For the finishing touch, stick the feather to the back of your bottle with sticky tape. Let's bowl!

What a shot!

That was a close one!

45

Grass head

Bring the outside inside with this hilarious grass head. As time goes by, your grass head's hair will grow even crazier!

Doodle Drawers

cotton wool

paper cup

scissors

3 elastic bands

2 googly eyes

a pair of tights

glue stick

wool

grass seeds

Be patient – your grass may take a little while to grow.

1 There's no time to waste so let's get going! Cut one foot off of your pair of tights. Be careful because scissors are sharp.

2 Put some grass seeds down into the toe of your tight. Push some cotton wool into the tight and on top of the seeds.

3 Tie a knot in the end of your tight. This is your head. Pinch out a nose and wind an elastic band round it to fix it in place.

4 Make an ear on either side of the head in the same way. This is a bit fiddly so you might want an adult to help.

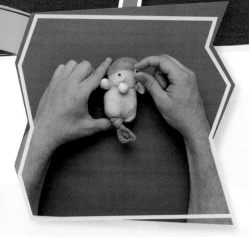

5 Stick two googly eyes on the front of your head. Don't worry if you don't have googly eyes – draw some eyes on white paper and cut them out.

6 Cut a small piece of wool and stick it under the nose in a nice big smiley shape. You could always use a pipe cleaner if you don't have any wool.

7 Put your grass head in a cup and water it every day. Within a week it will start sprouting grass – or hair!

When your grass head has grown enough hair, you can give it a haircut – or just let it grow wild! Don't grass heads look great?

I like your hairdo!

My making time's over but yours is just beginning!

LONDON, NEW YORK,
MELBOURNE, MUNICH, AND DELHI

Senior Editor Laura Gilbert
Senior Designer Lynne Moulding
Managing Editor Catherine Saunders
Art Director Lisa Lanzarini
Publishing Manager Simon Beecroft
Category Publisher Alex Allan
Photographer Andy Crawford
Photoshoot Assistant Rhys Thomas
Craft Makers John DeGray, Laura Gilbert,
Julia March and Lynne Moulding
Production Editor Clare McLean
Production Controller Amy Bennett

First published in Great Britain in 2009 by
Dorling Kindersley Limited,
80 Strand, London, WC2R ORL

Mister Maker ™ & © 2009 The Foundation.
Licensed by RDF Rights.
Page design copyright © 2009 Dorling Kindersley Limited
A Penguin Company

2 4 6 8 10 9 7 5 3 1
MD585 - 09/08

A CIP catalogue record for this book is available
from the British Library

ISBN: 978-1-40533-905-6

Colour reproduction by Media Development and Printing Ltd, UK
Printed and bound by L-Rex, China

DK would like to thank: Rachel Barke, Alison Carney, Tamsin
McArdle and Demi Charalambous at RDF Rights;
Rhys Thomas for his help on the shoot; and Andy Crawford
for the fabulous photography.

Discover more at
www.dk.com